Jesse James Rides

Written By
Arthur Prince

Illustrated By
Alan Howell

Alexander Press

ISBN 1-895335-00-0
Copyright©2000 Alexander Press Ltd.
Published by Alexander Press Ltd.
Toronto, Ont.
(416) 979-7886 fax, e-mail alexpress@aei.ca

Chapter 1

During the American Civil War, many citizens in the state of Missouri were divided as to which side to support. Some citizens supported President Lincoln and the Federal side. Others supported the Confederate cause.

Jesse James and his family, who had a farm in the town of Kearny, supported the Confederate side.

In 1863, Jesse's older brother, Frank, was fighting with William Quantrill, who led a band of Confederate guerrillas. These guerrillas, or bushwackers, as they were frequently called, raided Federal strongholds in Missouri and Kansas.

One day, in June 1863, the farmhouse of Jesse James' family was surrounded by 75 Federal militiamen. A group of them burst into the house pointing their pistols at Mrs. Zerelda James, Jesse's mother, and Dr. Reuben Samuel, his stepfather.

"Where is your boy, Frank?" one Federal officer demanded.

"I think he's in San Francisco," Mrs. James replied.

"San Francisco? A likely story!" the officer answered.

"We know he's with Quantrill," a second officer barked.

"Where is Quantrill's camp?" another Federal officer demanded.

"We don't know anything about Quantrill," Dr. Samuel replied nervously.

"Liars!" answered the Federal officer. "We know you are all Southern sympathizers supplying the bushwackers with food and information. We also know your son, Frank, is with Quantrill."

"All we know is that Frank went to San Francisco," insisted Dr. Samuel.

"Nonsense!" answered the other officer. "String him up and he'll tell us the truth."

The other militiamen took Dr. Samuel outside, put a noose around his neck, and then threw the rope around a tree limb and raised him up.

"All right. Now tell us where your son is," the officer demanded.

The soldiers let Dr. Samuel down and loosened the noose.

"I've told you, San Francisco," replied Dr. Samuel.

"String him up again boys," the officer ordered.

Once more Dr. Samuel was strung up and then lowered. Now he was gasping for air and could not talk.

The soldiers confronted Mrs. James.

"We've told you all we know," Mrs. James insisted.

"Let's find their younger son, Jesse," one officer said.

"Maybe he'll be more cooperative," said another.

The Federal soldiers found young Jesse, who was just seventeen years old, plowing a field.

"Where's your brother, Frank? The officer asked.

"He's in San Francisco, " Jesse replied.

" We know he's with Quantrill and we know you all help those bushwackers, " the officer said.

"Oh, no, we don't help Quantrill at all," Jesse replied.

"Liars! You're all liars!" the officer said. "Beat him!"

The other soldiers started to beat Jesse with their bayonets and rifle butts, but he clung to his story. The officers finally realized that they would not be able to obtain any useful information on Quantrill.

"We'll be back," one of the officers promised as the soldiers rode off.

Jesse returned to the farmhouse and cut down his stepfather from the tree limb.

" I think it's about time I joined Frank," Jesse announced to his mother.

" You can't," his mother replied. "You're too young."

"I'm old enough," Jesse insisted.

"You're much too young," Dr. Samuel said. "Besides, it's too dangerous."

"I'm seventeen," Jesse said. "I can ride and I can shoot straight. That's all Quantrill wants to know. If I stay here, the next time the Federals return, they'll take me away."

Chapter 2

Next morning Jesse saddled up his horse, took some provisions, and two Colt revolvers. He said good-bye to his family and rode off in the direction where he thought Quantrill was encamped.

Jesse rode from daybreak to sunset. Sometimes he would stop and ask for information from the farmers in the area. They were all Southern sympathizers and when they were convinced that Jesse wasn't a Federal spy, they gladly provided him with the information he sought.

On the second day, Jesse was watering his horse by a stream, when he was surrounded by two armed men.

"Put your hands up," one said pointing his revolver at Jesse while the other man disarmed him.

"Who are you?" the man asked.

"I'm Jesse James. I've a brother named Frank, who is with Quantrill and I mean to join up," Jesse said emphatically.

"A likely story," the other man said sceptically. " You look like a Federal spy to me."

" I've told you the truth," Jesse insisted.

"You could be lying," the bushwacker answered. "Besides, you're too young. Return home to your farm."

Just then, Jesse knocked the revolver out of the bushwacker's hand and picked it up from the ground. Now he pointed it at both of them.

"I'm Jesse James and I mean to join up," Jesse said. "Now take me to Quantrill, pronto."

"Well, all right, you win, kid," the bushwacker said admitting defeat.

Just then, four men came out of the bush, each with a rifle trained on Jesse.

"Drop you pistol, varmint," one of them ordered.

Jesse dropped the revolver.

"That's Jesse James," one of the bushwackers said. "I've seen him with his brother, Frank, before. He's all right. We can take him to Quantrill."

"If you say so," one of the guerrillas replied, "then it's safe to take him with us."

The bushwackers lowered their rifles. Jesse could now pick up his revolvers and mount his horse.

They all rode for Quantrill's camp which was well hidden in the bush. It didn't take too long to reach it. Only a small trail led to it. All along the way, they were met by heavily armed sentries.

When Jesse reached the camp, he found his brother, Frank, who was very much surprised to see him.

"Jesse, it's good to see you," Frank said as he hugged his brother. "But what are you doing here? You should be on the farm."

"I mean to join up," Jesse replied.

"Don't be foolish," Frank answered. " You're too young. Return to the farm."

"I can't," Jesse replied. "The Federals were there. They said they would come back. And when they do, I know they are going to take me away."

"In that case, I'd better introduce you to Quantrill," Frank answered.

The two brothers walked for awhile until they found the guerrilla leader.

"Bill," Frank said by way of introduction. "This here's my kid brother, Jesse."

"He's too young," Quantrill snapped. "Return to your farm, boy."

"I can ride," Jesse said, " and I can shoot."

Just then he whipped out his revolver from his holster in one blazing motion and shot several tin cans lying around a campfire some twenty yards away. He hit all of them.

"Mighty good shooting, kid," Quantrill said. " You'll do."

"You made a good impression on him," Frank said proudly.

" I owe it all to you," Jesse replied modestly. "You taught me to shoot when I was little."

"You're still little." Frank answered. " How old are you now?"

"Seventeen, going on eighteen," Jesse replied.

"Let's get some grub," Frank suggested.

The two brothers walked over to a campfire where several bushwackers were cooking.

"This here's my kid brother, Jesse," Frank said as he introduced him.

" I see the family resemblance," one bushwacker observed.

"Good shooting, kid. Mighty impressive," another one complimented Jesse.

"Why, thank you," Jesse replied modestly. "I learned it all from my brother."

"What made you join up?" another asked.

"The Yankees visited our farm," Jesse replied. "They're mighty nasty now. They figure that if we're not with them, then we must be against them. They're starting to treat us folk pretty harsh, now."

After the meal, Frank showed Jesse to his tent.

"It's a difficult life, being a bushwacker," Frank said. "We have to be prepared to break camp at a moment's notice. The Yankees can't find us if we move around a lot. Conditions aren't very comfortable, either, as you see."

"I' ll get used to it," Jesse replied. " Just as you have."

"Whatever you do," Frank cautioned, " don't be a hothead. That's one way you'll be a goner before your time."

"Fine advice, Frank" Jesse replied.

Jesse James did not have long to wait before he saw action.

The next day, a picket rode into camp and breathlessly announced that he had spotted a Federal cavalry patrol.

"How many Yankees are there?" Quantrill asked.

"About twenty," the picket replied.

"OK, let's saddle up and ambush them," Quantrill ordered.

The bushwackers prepared for the upcoming battle. They checked their weapons and ammunition. Then they rode out.

"Jesse," Frank said, " just stick with me and don't do anything foolish."

The guerrillas rode in the direction where the Federal cavalry patrol had been spotted. Finally they came upon the soldiers.

They prepared for the ambush and hid among the trees. Quantrill waited until the Federals came within range of the bushwackers' rifles.

"Fire!" Quantrill shouted.

Immediately a hail of bullets greeted the Federals.

" You can shoot now, Jesse," Frank told his brother.

Jesse aimed carefully and picked off a Federal trooper who fell from his horse. A number of the Federal soldiers were wounded. The bushwackers suffered two wounded, as well.

The Federals, surprised by the sudden ambush, beat a hasty retreat as they helped their wounded.

After a short shoot out, Quantrill gave the signal for the bushwackers to retreat, as well.

Chapter 3

When October arrived, the trees started to lose their leaves and the forests no longer provided the bushwackers with cover which they needed for their guerrilla raids.

Every year at this time, the bushwackers headed south to Texas. Quantrill's force, numbering some 400 men, slowly made their way south through Kansas and then reached Baxter Springs, just five miles from Indian Territory.

Dave Pool led the scouts, which rode ahead of the main column. Pool managed to capture a supply wagon driven by two Federal soldiers. The soldiers were interrogated and said they were stationed at Fort Blair, near Baxter Springs.

Pool rode back to the main column to tell Quantrill what he had learned.

"A Fort Blair?" Quantrill exclaimed. "That's news to me."

"The Federals just built it six months ago," Pool explained.

"Then it looks like we are going to have to capture that fort," Quantrill said. "I want you and Bill Gregg to lead your men in a charge. I will hold back the main force in reserve and use it only if necessary."

"I'll tell Bill the plan," Pool said.

Pool rode over to Bill Gregg and informed him about the battle plan Quantrill had drawn up. With Gregg were Jesse and Frank James.

When Pool gave the signal, the bushwackers charged the fort firing at the surprised Federal troops who had been lounging outside the fort. As soon as they saw the guerrillas riding toward them, the Union soldiers ran for the fort as fast as they could.

Frank and Jesse James rode fearlessly at the Federals, firing their Colts at the running soldiers. When Jesse emptied one Colt, he reached for another Colt in his belt and fired with an incredible accuracy.

However, most of the Union soldiers managed to make it back to the fort, even if they had been hit. From the fort, the Federals organized a blistering fire with their carbines. And soon a howitzer cannon was mobilized for action against the Confederate guerrillas. With shells exploding all around them, the bushwackers started to retreat.

"Everyone back!" Gregg ordered.

The guerrillas withdrew beyond the range of the cannon.

" I certainly wasn't expecting that cannon," Frank said to his brother as they beat a hasty retreat.

"It sure was a surprise," Jesse offered.

"No more charges, men," Pool shouted. "Keep out of range of their guns."

In the meantime, Quantrill's men, who were all wearing blue Federal uniforms they had captured at another engagement, spied a Federal column of some 100 soldiers heading towards Fort Blair. This troop was commanded by Major General James Blunt.

Seeing what looked to him as a Federal cavalry unit sent out from Fort Blair as a welcoming party, General Blunt was most pleased. At the head of General Blunt's column was a bandwagon of musicians.

General Blunt had been too far from Fort Blair to hear the noise of the battle.

"Musicians," General Blunt ordered. " Prepare to commence playing when the welcoming party arrives."

As General Blunt peered at the welcoming party, however, he became increasingly apprehensive. He saw some officers riding up and down the line as if they were preparing for battle.

Consequently he sent two of his officers forward to take a closer look. In a short time they raced back with the news that they were facing guerrillas. General Blunt wasn't very worried, however.

"It's just a few of Jackman's guerrillas from South Missouri," General Blunt said confidently. "Give them a few rounds and they'll run off for cover."

Quantrill rode along the length of the line, preparing his men for battle. He ordered a messenger to report to Bill Gregg that they had come across a Federal column and that he was to bring his men from Fort Blair to join in this attack. Only Dave Pool and his men were to remain at the fort.

Quantrill took off his hat, stuffed it inside his coat, and spurred his horse forward.

"Come on, boys," he shouted.

The guerrillas galloped forward towards the Federal column shouting rebel yells. Four hundred charging bushwackers firing at one hundred Union troops caused immediate panic among the latter.

Stricken with mortal fear, all the Federal soldiers turned tail and rode back across the prairie. Only General Blunt was left to face the attacking bushwackers. He rode after his men calling them cowards and urging them to turn around and fight. But they refused to listen and rode away.

One by one, the Federal troops were run down and shot, most of them at a ravine where their horses were not able to leap over.

One of the guerrillas, Bill Bledsoe, overtook the musicians' wagon and ordered them to surrender. A Federal soldier on the wagon shot at Bledsoe who fell off his horse.

"Fletch," Bledsoe called to his fellow bushwacker. "That outfit have shot me. Take my two pistols and shoot them all."

Fletch Taylor with several other bushwackers took off after the bandwagon which was traveling at a frantic pace as it tried to escape. Soon the left front wheel hit a rock and fell off, forcing the musicians to tumble out of the wagon. Panic-stricken they all waved their white handkerchiefs as a sign of surrender.

Both General Blunt and Major Henry Curtis tried to rally their men to hold a line and fight the guerrillas. Major Curtis galloped west on a parallel course with General Blunt.

Soon they came to a wide deep gully. The general's horse made the leap. But just as Major Curtis' horse was about to leap, it was shot in the hip throwing the officer off it.

A bushwacker had pursued Major Curtis across the prairie and managed to take the officer prisoner.

After the battle was over, Quantrill went to Fort Blair where he met his two officers, George Todd and Bill Anderson.

"I say let's attack the fort again," Todd urged.

"Are you plumb loco?" Quantrill replied. "It would be too costly and we'd lose 15-20 men, at least."

"I say let's attack the fort again and burn it down," Anderson said.

"No, let's bluff their surrender." Quantrill said. "Todd, go to the fort and demand they surrender."

"Good idea," Todd agreed.

Todd made up a white flag and waved it, which meant he wanted a temporary truce for a parley. The fort responded with a white flag.

Todd went up to the fort and demanded to speak to the commander.

"I'm representing Colonel Quantrill and I demand that you surrender Fort Blair," Todd said.

"Never!" replied Lieutenant Pond, commander of Fort Blair.

"In that case," Todd suggested, " we wish to exchange prisoners with you."

"We have no prisoners," Lieutenant Pond replied curtly.

"I shall confer with my commander," Todd answered.

Todd rode back to Quantrill.

"The Federal lieutenant said he won't surrender and he has no prisoners," Todd reported.

"It's obvious he saw through our bluff," Quantrill replied. "We should continue south. We have done enough damage for today."

Quantrill's force headed south. Later at dusk, scouts reported they had seen a wagon train with Creek Indians, who were on the Federal side.

The bushwackers planned to attack them. As soon as the Indians came within range, the bushwackers poured a withering fire at them.

When the battle was over, the guerrillas looked through the wagons to see if they could use any of the supplies, but found little of value.

A few days later, the bushwackers crossed the Red River into Texas. They established their winter camp at Mineral Springs, near the town of Sherman.

They built some simple log cabins to keep out the cold and secured a supply of meat. Being in Confederate territory, the guerrillas could now relax and didn't have to worry about being ambushed by Union patrols.

Chapter 4

Jesse and Frank James enjoyed meeting the local girls at the numerous dances they were invited to.

"We've heard quite a lot about Quantrill and his men," one girl said to Jesse at a dance.

"Oh, I'm sure our exploits have been greatly exaggerated," Jesse replied.

"You're being much too modest," the girl responded.

"We don't like to brag," Frank interjected, "but we only do what Quantrill orders us to carry out."

"Some say you bushwackers are nothing but common cutthroats," another girl said. "But you all seem to be very nice Southern gentlemen."

"Quantrill has told us to be on our best behavior while in Texas," Jesse explained.

"I'm Sara and these are my friends Phoebe and Vanessa," one of the girls said by way of introduction.

"Care to dance, Phoebe? "Frank asked.

"With pleasure," Phoebe replied.

Frank and Phoebe headed for the dance floor while another bushwacker asked Vanessa for a dance. This left Jesse and Sara alone.

"You sure are pretty," Jesse said rather boldly.

"I'll bet you say that to all the girls," Sara replied with a blush.

"I mean that sincerely," Jesse answered.

"How old are you?" Sara asked.

"Twenty-one," Jesse lied.

"Come now, you can't possibly be more than seventeen," Sara responded.

"It's that obvious? I may be young but I'm very mature," Jesse answered. "And how old are you?"

"Don't you know, a gentleman never asks a lady her age?" Sara said. "It's not proper etiquette."

"Pardon me, I forgot my manners," Jesse replied. "I'm a simple farm boy from Missouri."

"Do you want to dance?" Sara asked.

"I'd rather sit this one out," Jesse replied.

"You do know how to dance?" Sara asked.

"I do, but I'm not very good," Jesse replied. "Mainly I come here to socialize."

"You boys must like us Texas gals," Sara said with a laugh.

"You're all so very charming," Jesse replied.

"Would you like to go for a stroll outside?" Sara suggested.

"I was about to suggest that myself," Jesse replied.

"It's too noisy and smoky here," Sara said.

Jesse and Sara walked outside. It was a lovely night. There was some moonlight. And one felt a light breeze.

As they strolled the noise and the music seemed to fade in the background.

"Fresh air," Sara said. "I was almost ready to faint from that stale tobacco smoke."

"It sure is peaceful here," Jesse observed.

"If only the war was over," Sara said. "So many of our fine Texas boys are off fighting far away."

"I'll bet you must have a boyfriend," Jesse asked.

"I have a number of admirers," Sara said coquettishly.

"A pretty girl such as you," Jesse said, " you probably have a dozen admirers."

"Not that many," Sara replied.

"I wish the war was over, too," Jesse said. "It's been going on for too long. Perhaps peace will come soon, before we lose too many good men."

"What's that noise, coming from the dance? Sara asked.

"Sounds like a fight," Jesse said. "I'm afraid some of the bushwackers have had too much to drink and are acting rowdy. I apologize for their bad behavior."

"It's time for me to return to find my friends," Sara said.

"Will I see you again?" Jesse asked.

"I come to these dances regularly," Sara said.

Jesse and Sara returned to the dance and they found their friends. They both said good-bye until the next time.

When a band of Comanchee Indians attacked Gainesville, the Confederate General McCullough ordered Quantrill and his men to go after them.

"Saddle up, boys," Quantrill ordered his men, "we're heading for Gainesville."

Jesse and Frank and the other bushwackers were eager for action since by now they had become bored in Texas.

"Be careful, Jesse," Frank cautioned his brother. "This time we'll be fighting tough Comanchees, not Federals."

"We'll scatter the Comanchees as we did the Federals," Jesse assured Frank.

"Overconfidence will get you killed, Jesse," Frank cautioned his brother.

The column of bushwackers went forward and in two days they reached Gainesville. But they found no Comanchees. Quantrill asked a citizen for information.

" The Comanchees left," the citizen replied. "They shot up the town, burnt a few houses and then hightailed out. They wounded a few of our townspeople, but none too seriously. Fortunately no one was killed."

"Which way did the Comanchees head?" Quantrill asked.

"They headed Northwest," the citizen replied.

Quantrill and his men followed the Comanchees' tracks for a few days, but eventually they lost the trail. A discouraged Quantrill ordered his men to return to their base camp.

"General McCullough isn't going to like this one bit," Qauntrill said to his men glumly. "The Comanchees just plain outfoxed us."

"We're not experienced Indian fighters," Frank reminded Jesse.

Chapter 5

When spring came, it was time for Quantrill's men to head back to Missouri. In early April, the guerrillas started to move north.

It was a rainy spring, so all the rivers and streams were swollen. The horses had to swim across them. There was mud everywhere.

With great difficulty, Quantrill's men rode northwards. Finally they reached Missouri and set up camp in Jackson County.

There they encountered Federal militias and troops of the 2nd and 3rd Colorado Cavalry regiments who hunted the bushwackers relentlessly.

There were numerous skirmishes, but whenever a large force of Union troops arrived, Quantrill ordered his men to slip away through the forests, avoiding pitched battles.

One day, a visitor arrived at Quantrill's camp. He was John Chestnut, an agent sent by the Confederate General Sterling Price.

"General Price," Chestnut informed Quantrill at a meeting, "will be invading Missouri and he wants your men to disrupt Union defenses by cutting telegraph wires and blowing up trains and bridges."

"How large is his Army?" Quantrill asked.

"General Price has 12,000 troops," Chestnut said with an air of confidence.

"That's mighty impressive," answered George Todd somewhat skeptically.

"What is his objective?" Quantrill asked.

"General Price intends to march through Missouri and capture St. Louis," Chestnut said confidently.

"That will be no easy task," Quantrill said, " even with 12,000 troops."

"If your men can wreak havoc behind Federal lines," Chestnut said, " it will be of immense service to us."

"We'll do our best," Quantrill promised.

That night Quantrill and Todd made plans to attack the town of Keytesville.

"How many Federal troops are there in Keytesville?" Quantrill asked Todd.

"My sources tell me no more than 35 troopers," Todd replied.

"They are no match for our 130 men, then," Quantrill answered. "We'll attack tomorrow morning. Inform the men."

In the morning the bushwackers saddled up and began their ride to Keytesville.

Jesse and Frank James rode beside one another. They chatted as they rode.

"Be careful, Jesse," Frank cautioned his brother. "The Union troops are heavily armed. Don't do anything foolish."

"I'll be sure to cover you, Frank," Jesse promised.

When Quantrill's force arrived in Keytesville, the unarmed citizens scattered as soon as they saw the bushwackers. However, in the north end of the town stood a brick courthouse occupied by 35 Federal troops. This was a formidable structure.

"Let's show them our total force and surround the town," Quantrill suggested. "Perhaps we can scare them into surrendering."

The bushwackers now completely surrounded the town from all sides, but kept a safe distance beyond gunfire range from the courthouse.

"Todd, take a flag of truce," Quantrill ordered, "and demand that they surrender the garrison."

Todd took a white flag, waved it a few times, and then rode up to the courthouse when he saw that the Union troops did the same.

"Lookee here," Todd said to the Union officer who came out of the courthouse to meet him. "You are completely surrounded. If we have to fight you, we will and we'll burn down the entire town. If, however, you surrender now, we'll parole all of you. The choice is yours. Do you want to live or do you want to die?"

"I'll have to speak with my men," Lieutenant Anthony Pleyer, the Union officer, replied.

The Federal lieutenant surrendered and Quantrill burned the courthouse down.

Chapter 6

A few days after the Keytesville success, Quantrill held a meeting with his two most trusted lieutenants, George Todd and Bill Anderson.

"I say we attack Fayette," Anderson proposed.

"The town is too heavily defended," cautioned Quantrill.

"If we all wear the Federal uniforms we captured in Keytesville," suggested Todd, "we'll be able to surprise the town and trick the Union soldiers stationed there."

"They'll realize soon enough, who we are," Quantrill said.

Despite their initial disagreements, the leaders set their differences aside and made plans to attack Fayette.

The next morning, the bushwackers saddled up and rode to Fayette, all of them wearing blue Federal uniforms.

"Do you think our Federal uniforms will fool them?" Jesse asked his brother, Frank, who was riding beside him.

"At first, perhaps," Frank replied.

"When I give the signal, boys," Anderson shouted, "charge and shoot up the town. Head for the north end, where the Federals are. OK, now charge!"

Jesse and Frank rode behind Anderson. The bushwackers shot in the air, scattering the townspeople.

As he was riding, Jesse spotted a man aiming a rifle at the bushwackers, but Jesse shot him before he could shoot. Frank picked off another citizen firing a rifle.

Soon the guerrillas reached the north end of town where the Federals were located in a log blockhouse on a ridge. Jesse and Frank were in the first charge led by Anderson. They fired their revolvers at the blockhouse but their bullets merely lodged harmlessly in the thick logs.

The Federal soldiers could not be seen, only the muzzles of their rifles protruding through portholes. The Federals poured a withering fire on the attacking bushwackers. Horses went down, as did many guerrillas.

Jesse and Frank managed to survive the first charge. Then a second charge was led by George Todd. All around him, many of his men were felled by the Federal fire.

Frustrated and angry, Todd retreated, regrouped and led another charge, only to have his men cut down once more.

Todd and Anderson rode up to Quantrill and urged him to lead another charge with the men he held in reserve.

"One more charge and we'll take the blockhouse," Anderson said.

"We'll never succeed," Quantrill said. "It's too heavily fortified. We'll lose good men for no reason."

"You're a coward!" Anderson shouted at Quantrill.

"I ain't loco," Quantrill replied. "I told you that charging that blockhouse was stupid."

"You're yeller," Todd accused him.

"No, I just don't want my men killed for nothing," Quantrill replied.

"I'll have to agree with Bill," Frank James offered in defense of his leader.

"Me, too," Jesse James added. "We didn't even see the Yankees. Our bullets just stuck in the logs. We didn't hit any of them."

Finally the bushwackers admitted defeat. They buried their dead and cared for their wounded. They returned to their camp, morale at a low.

It took some time for the bushwackers to lick their wounds. Fayette was their worst defeat.

One evening, around the campfire, the mood was very gloomy.

"If you ask me," one bushwacker said, "I don't know what the point of this war is. The Confederacy is losing the war."

"You're right," another bushwacker agreed.

"That's a defeatist attitude," Jesse said.

"I'm simply being realistic," the bushwacker replied.

"The South has no chance of winning the war," another guerrilla offered. "We simply don't have the resources which the North has. This war is as good as lost."

At this point Quantrill came to the campfire. He sensed that the mood was grim. "If any of you wish to leave, you can. I won't stop you. Nor will I accuse any of you of cowardice. Whoever wishes to leave, can head out at daybreak."

new horse, it reared and bucked. He called out for help from his men. Dick Glasscock and Clark Hockensmith heard him and reined in. They fired at the Federals while Quantrill ran to catch up.

Quantrill reached Glasscock's horse just as it was hit and went down. Then he ran to Hockensmith, but he took a bullet in his back and fell to the ground. One of Terrill's men confronted Quantrill and shot off his trigger finger.

"It is useless to shoot any more," Quantrill said. "I am a dying man."

Quantrill was disarmed of his Colts and carried into the parlor of the Wakefield house where he was laid on the couch.

"Who are you?" Captain Terrill asked.

"I am Captain Clarke of the Fourth Missouri Cavalry," Quantrill lied. "Look in my pocket and you'll find a gold watch and $500. It's yours, if you'll just let me stay here. I'm a dying man."

"Agreed," Terrill said pocketing the watch and money.

Captain Terrill told Wakefield that he was leaving to fetch a wagon. "You are responsible for insuring that Captain Clarke stays here. I will return with a wagon so we can take him to a hospital."

Terrill's men left. Later Wakefield called a local doctor.

During the night Jesse and Frank James, with two other bushwackers had slipped back to the house and offered to spirit Quantrill away.

"Frank," Quantrill said, "I have run a long time, but

they have got me at last. It is impossible for me to get well. The war is over and in reality I am a dying man, so let me alone."

"We can take you to Samuel's Depot where the Yankees would never be able to find you," Jesse James said.

"No, I will die, and it is no use. Good-bye." Quantrill said.

Realizing that they couldn't convince Quantrill, Jesse and Frank and the other bushwackers left without him.

The next day, Terrill and his men returned with a Conestoga wagon drawn by two mules. Straw was thrown in the back of the wagon where Quantrill was placed.

Terrill's men formed a column and the wagon set off for Louisville. A short while later, Quantrill died in a Louisville hospital.

Chapter 10

By now the American Civil War was over. Jesse and Frank James and the other bushwackers surrendered to the Federal authorities and were pardoned.

Many bushwackers harbored a grudge against the Yankees and found it difficult to adapt to peacetime America.

Jesse James was among these bushwackers. He was determined that somehow he should continue to fight the Yankees. Only by becoming an outlaw could he do so.

When the war was over, Jesse and Frank James returned to their family farm in Missouri and resumed farming. But farming had no appeal to the ambitious Jesse. One day, while the two brothers were plowing a field, they had a discussion.

"This farming doesn't have much to offer us," Jesse said to his brother. "It's very hard work and at the end of a year we barely make a living, if we are lucky."

"It's an honest living," replied Frank. "I wouldn't complain."

"The problem with you," Jesse said, " is that you have no vision."

"No, I'm just sensible," Frank replied. "You're a dreamer."

"I guess I'm just not cut out for this hard work," Jesse

countered. "If I had money, I would start a business in town, maybe a saloon, something which was easier and made a lot more money."

"Well, you don't," Frank replied. "So stop dreaming."

"Look, Frank," Jesse suggested, " we could get a lot more money if we really wanted to."

"How?" Frank asked his curiosity piqued.

"We could rob a bank," Jesse responded

"Rob a bank?" Frank exclaimed. "Are you plumb loco?"

"No, I'm not," Jesse replied. "We could round up some of our old bushwacker friends. It wouldn't be hard since we're all good with guns."

Frank remained skeptical for weeks. However eventually Jesse was able to convince the reluctant Frank.

One day they decided to visit some of their bushwacker friends. They rode out to the farm of the Younger brothers. There lived Cole, Robert, Jim, and John.

After some pleasantries, Jesse proposed his idea to the Younger brothers. "Look, fellers, ain't none of us going to get rich from farming."

"What do you suggest?" asked Cole Younger.

"I propose we all rob a bank," Jesse said.

"Rob a bank?" Jim Younger blurted out as he started to laugh. "Has the sun fried your brains, Jesse?"

The other brothers started to laugh, too.

"My brother is most serious," Frank answered in Jesse's defense. " And you fellers can only laugh at him."

"Surely, you can't be serious, Jesse?" Robert Younger asked.

"I'm very serious," Jesse replied. "If you fellers wish to remain poor the rest of your lives, well, that's your decision, but as for us, we're going ahead with our plan. And we're going to find other bushwacker friends who think the way we do."

"You are most audacious, Jesse," John Younger said, "but, I'm beginning to think you know what you're talking about."

"Which bank do you propose robbing?" Cole Younger asked.

"The Clay County Savings Bank in Liberty," Jesse replied. "I've been watching that bank for some time and I know it has a lot of money, Yankee money."

"You figure us six could pull it off?" John Younger asked.

"No, we need another six," Jesse said, " but I'm sure I can round up more bushwackers."

"Count me in," Cole Younger said.

" Count us all in," Jim Younger said speaking for his brothers, as well.

"When I get all the men together," Jesse said " we'll have another parley and plan the robbery in detail."

Jesse and Frank said good-bye to the Youngers and rode off.

Jesse recruited more bushwackers until he had a dozen men. A meeting was called for at the James farm where all the men came.

"We have to carry out the bank robbery with military precision," Jesse said. "We must view it as a Quantrill raid."

"We're all very experienced gunmen," George Shepherd reminded Jesse.

"Yes, but not experienced in robbing banks," Frank replied. "Let's not be overconfident. Any number of things can go wrong."

"Here's the plan I've drawn up," Jesse said, as he unfurled a drawing of the bank and the town. "Frank and me, wearing Federal soldier uniforms, will enter the bank and ask for change. Then we'll rob it. We don't want more men entering the bank because that will only arouse suspicion. Instead I want all of you to place yourselves in strategic positions around town and cover our retreat when we come out. There may be some fireworks."

" I love the Fourth of July fireworks display," Jim Younger said. "Excellent plan, Jesse."

"You're a genius," Oliver Shepherd added.

" Don't start counting the money, yet, fellers," Frank warned. "It will be harder than you think."

Chapter 11

The bank robbery was set for two days after the last meeting. On February 13th 1866, it was unusually cold in Liberty, Missouri.

Jesse and Frank James rode ahead while groups of other bushwackers trailed behind at a discreet distance so as not to arouse suspicion. Slowly the riders entered Liberty. Most of them posted themselves at strategic positions in town and scanned the citizens to see if they suspected something was up.

Jesse and Frank, along with the Youngers, rode to the bank. Jesse and Frank dismounted and entered the bank, while the Youngers held the horses outside.

In the bank, Frank walked over to the stove to warm himself, while Jesse approached the bank clerk.

"I should like to change this $100 bill," Jesse asked politely.

"Certainly," the clerk answered.

Just as the clerk was about to change the bill, Jesse and Frank jumped over the counter. They pointed their revolvers at the startled clerk.

"If you make any noise," Jesse warned, "we'll shoot you."

"We want all your money! Quick!" Frank demanded.

The two bank clerks were forced into the vault and ordered to put all the money into a sack. This they did without hesitation. Frank scooped up all the money he could find in the cashiers' drawers and put it into the sack.

Jesse and Frank then closed the vault door on the clerks, but it failed to lock. Then they dashed out of the bank and jumped on their waiting horses. The two clerks managed to escape from the vault and rushed outside the bank.

"The bank's been robbed!" one clerk shouted. "The bank's been robbed!"

Two other passersby now called out that the bank had been robbed. The bandits began shooting at them, hitting one of them.

Other bandits on horseback started to shoot in the air to disperse the citizens. Then they rode out of town as fast as their horses would carry them.

Soon a posse was organized to go after the bandits. The posse followed the robbers' tracks for a few miles, but then a blinding snowstorm began and it became impossible to follow the tracks.

The bandits rode to their planned destination, an abandoned farmhouse. A couple sentries were posted outside and the rest of the gang entered the house.

"Well, Jesse," Cole Younger said with eager anticipation. "Let's see what we got."

"The sack is heavy," Jesse said. "We got a lot of money."

The sack was opened and all the money was dumped